Cold Rose
Rosa tiene frío

by Deborah Schecter

ISBN: 978-1-338-70280-4
Illustrated by Anne Kennedy
Copyright © 2020 by Deborah Schecter. All rights reserved.
Published by Scholastic Inc., 557 Broadway, New York, NY 10012

10 9 8 7 6   68   23 24 25 26/0

Printed in Jiaxing, China. First printing, June 2020.

Cold clothes.

La ropa, fría.

Cold nose.

La nariz, fría.

Cold toes.
Cold Rose!

Los dedos, fríos.
¡Rosa tiene frío!

Warm clothes.

La ropa, calentita.

Warm toes.

Los dedos, calentitos.

Warm nose.

La nariz, calentita.

Warm Rose!

¡Rosa está calentita!